The SECRET ELEPHANT

The true story of an extraordinary wartime friendship

Ellan Rankin

wren &rook

Our story begins many years ago, back when I was a baby elephant.

Screeching monkeys dangled in their trees, roaring lions sunbathed on a dusty patch of dried grass and sniffling meerkats patrolled their enclosure.

There were no other elephants like me at the zoo. But I did have my keeper and she was my family.

We did EVERYTHING together. We had lunch together,

we washed together

and we even did chores together.

I was a VERY helpful young elephant.

But then everything changed.
People stopped visiting the zoo, and my
keeper told me about a great war that was coming.

At night, enormous
machines flew in the air
and dropped strange
things on the city.

Great bangs shook the
ground and flashes of orange
light burned across the sky.
I couldn't see the other
animals through the smoke.
I didn't understand what was
happening or where the loud
noises were coming from.

The huge blasts
hurt my ears.

I was alone.

My keeper knew
how scared I was of
the big explosions, so
she started sneaking into
the zoo after dark to keep
me company and rub my ears.

"We're living through a war, my
girl. I hope it will be over soon,
but until it is, I won't leave you
alone again, I promise . . .

I have a plan."

The next day, once the
head keeper had left . . .

. . . we crept and we creeped.

We sneaked
and we snuck'd.

I was a
VERY stealthy
young elephant.

My keeper took me all the way to her enclosure. It was even nicer than mine!

There were lots of plants to eat,

things to dust my skin with,

things to scratch itches with,

a new
watering hole

and new friends
to sing along with.

I won't even
tell you what I did
in the dining room.

I was home.

Every morning, we would
sneak back into the zoo.

Then, at night, we would
do it all over again . . .

Yes, our new secret routine
was working very nicely.

As time passed, I got
a little bigger . . .

. . . but I was still safe with my keeper.
If we were caught, I'd be sent back to the zoo
and I'd be alone again. Neither of us wanted that.

So even though I kept growing,

my keeper and I were sure that we could keep our special secret.

After all, I was still a VERY . . .

. . . quiet young elephant.

But our secret was out.

"It's not safe for you to stay here anymore, my girl," my keeper told me sadly. "I'm going to have to take you back. You should be at the zoo where you belong."

I thought,

You are my family.

I belong with you.

ELEPHANT CHARGE
DOG UNHARM

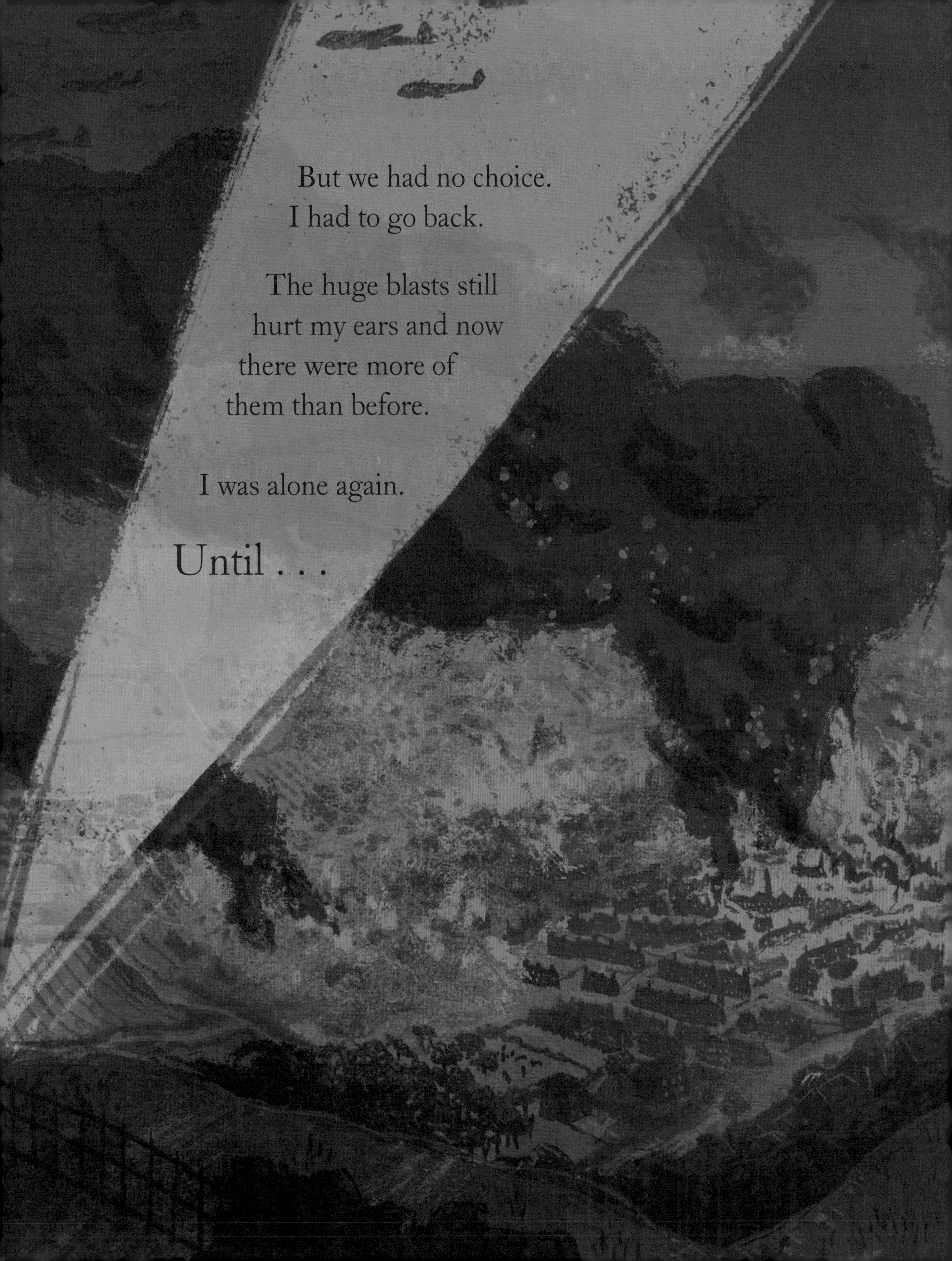

But we had no choice.
I had to go back.

The huge blasts still
hurt my ears and now
there were more of
them than before.

I was alone again.

Until . . .

She came back.

"I could never leave you, my girl.
You are my family. My home is with you."
And so we spent the rest of the war together.

We didn't have to wait much longer for the awful war to end. My keeper didn't need to stay with me and things at the zoo started to change.

The screeching monkeys, roaring lions and sniffling meerkats are all still here. But my keeper found me a family to keep me company.

Years have passed and she doesn't work here anymore. I miss her a lot. But she still finds time to visit. I hope she'll recognise me . . .

"We've both got a few more wrinkles now, don't we, my girl?"

The True Story of the Elephant and Her Keeper

THE SEARCH IS ON!

To celebrate its 75th anniversary in 2009, Belfast Zoo wanted to solve a curious mystery. Photographs had been found in the zoo archives showing a woman with a baby elephant in her back garden in Belfast during World War Two. So, the zoo launched a campaign to discover the identity of the 'elephant angel'.

It wasn't long before the truth was uncovered. The woman's name was Denise Weston Austin. She was one of the first female keepers at Belfast Zoo. She had rescued Sheila, a baby Asian elephant, and kept her at home during the war.

BELFAST ZOO AND WORLD WAR TWO

World War Two was one of the largest and most widespread battles in history. It began in 1939 and ended in 1945. Bombs were dropped on towns and cities across the UK, including Belfast.

The government were worried that a bomb would drop on Belfast Zoo and all the animals would escape, endangering lives. To protect the people of Belfast, they ordered for some of the zoo animals to be killed. But Denise, the 'elephant angel', was determined to protect Sheila, a baby elephant.

THE ELEPHANT IN THE GARDEN

When the zoo's head keeper left every night, Denise and Sheila would walk as far as Denise's house. Sometimes the pair would stop at the local shop for pieces of leftover stale bread. The two would then walk back to the zoo every morning, before the head keeper arrived.

Although residents had spotted Sheila on her walks, they didn't know for sure that Sheila was staying the night. It was a very well-kept secret, until Sheila chased a dog through a neighbour's fence. The neighbour went to the head keeper, who was shocked to discover Sheila's second home.

After that, Sheila had to remain at the zoo. But Denise wasn't going to abandon Sheila, and she visited Sheila at the zoo during air raids so that she could rub Sheila's ears to keep her calm. Denise continued to visit Sheila for the rest of her life, until Sheila's death more than twenty years after World War Two ended.

After all, they were family.

To my parents, teachers and everyone who got this book to here, thank you.

E. R.

First published in Great Britain in 2023 by Wren & Rook

A CIP catalogue record for this book is available from the British Library.

HB ISBN: 978 1 52636 383 1 PB ISBN: 978 1 52636 379 4

2 4 6 8 10 9 7 5 3 1

Wren & Rook
An imprint of Hachette Children's Group
Part of Hodder & Stoughton
Carmelite House, 50 Victoria Embankment, London EC4Y 0DZ

An Hachette UK Company
www.hachette.co.uk www.hachettechildrens.co.uk

Printed in China